Largo

1st movt from Sonata, op. 5 no. 9

Arcangelo Corelli
(1653–1713)

Do not play the repeats in the exam.

Ceciliana and Vivace

from Sonata no. 1

Willem de Fesch
(1687–1761)

Do not play the repeats in the exam.

Violin
Grade 4

Pieces

for Trinity College London exams

2016-2019

Published by
Trinity College London
www.trinitycollege.com

Registered in England
Company no. 02683033
Charity no. 1014792

Printed in England by Caligraving Ltd.

TCL 014849
ISBN 978-0-85736-457-9

9 780857 364579

Presto

3rd movt from Symphony no. 4

Arr. Richard Wade

J C Bach
(1735–1782)

Do not play the repeat in the exam.

Theme and Variation

from Caprice no. 24

Arr. Mary Cohen

Niccolò Paganini
(1782–1840)

Neapolitan Song

from *Swan Lake*

Arr. Paul de Keyser

Pyotr Tchaikovsky
(1840–1893)

Allegro con bravura [♩ = 82]

Rondo

from *Little School of Melody* op. 123

Arr. Mary Cohen

Charles Dancla
(1817–1907)

Smoke Gets in Your Eyes

Arr. Edward Huws Jones

Jerome Kern
(1885–1945)

Slow and expressive [♩ = 72]

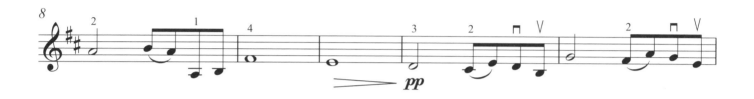

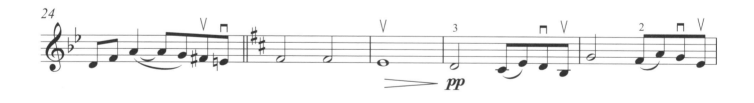

Leave-taking

Alfred Moffat
(1863–1950)

Rustic Dance

Christopher Norton
(born 1953)

The Fascinator

Arr. Edward Huws Jones

James Scott
(1885–1938)

Bracketed notes may be omitted in the exam.
Do not play the repeats in the exam, but do play the D. S. al Fine.